DATE DUE

DEMCO 38-296

it is the poem singing into your eyes

it is

the poem

singing

into your eyes

anthology

of new

young poets

edited by Arnold Adoff

HARPER & ROW, PUBLISHERS / New York, Evanston, San Francisco, London

Other Books by Arnold Adoff

BLACK ON BLACK
Commentaries by Negro Americans

BLACK OUT LOUD
An Anthology of Modern Poems by Black Americans

BROTHERS AND SISTERS
Modern Stories by Black Americans

CITY IN ALL DIRECTIONS
An Anthology of Modern Poems

I AM THE DARKER BROTHER
An Anthology of Modern Poems by Negro Americans

MALCOLM X

MA nDA LA

The editor wishes to thank the Innovation Team of the Education Development Center, Washington, D.C., for permission to use "I Feel So Muggy," by Cleave Reed (Poncho); **Hanging Loose Magazine,** for permission to use "The Field Madonna" by Susan Mernit; and **Motive** magazine, where "Clear," and "America Bleeds," by Angelo Lewis, first appeared. Personal thanks, also, to the hundreds of librarians, teachers, and magazine and book editors who responded with submissions, space, their time, and good vibrations.

designs by Faith Nicholas / photographs on pages 28, 76, and 94 by Edward E. Davis

Library of Congress Catalog Number: 79-157898
Standard Book Number 06-020087-1 (Trade)
Standard Book Number 06-020088-x (Harpercrest)

6555

For My Children,
        Leigh and Jaime
In Honor of My
        Wife, Virginia

it is very simple

It is very simple. You believe in the poem. You believe in the young poem
and the young poet. You want words to sing and mean and be
arranged into a form that can stand strong.

You look for typewriters that spit bullets and sprout roses. You look
for poets who can destroy language and thought and create from that
wreckage a new vision of reality. You look for poets who can
create life in the midst of a nation creating death.

You talk to your students and to their friends. And to friends of
friends. You write to hundreds of librarians and teachers and editors. You
write to young poets in high schools and in neighborhood workshops
and crash-pads in monster cities. You read. You listen to young
words singing. Into your eyes. Hitting between your eyes
with truth-bullets of love and breath and hot reasons.

A newspaper query brings in thousands of manuscripts. Your letter in
magazines brings in hundreds more. Poems fly in envelopes and boxes.
By class and library-group. From forty states, Canada, Denmark, Japan,
Mexico. Type and pencil and crayon scribbles on the backs of homework
sheets. In the end, more than 6,000 manuscripts, and who knows how
many thousands of poems. You take two years and read, listen, and write
for more poems. Then you make a book. You choose the finest poems,
ride them around and around and mold sections and sequence. You make
a book. The poems are the book. The poets are the book.

And the book is for the young poets. They are not afraid of open
eyes and feeling full of sun. They are not afraid to touch and shout and
pull things apart until they get to hot reasons and cold lies. They are the
witness-poets to the martyr/murders of their heroes. Their poems
come out of those open wounds that confront us all. And the
silent pains of every day that are not red.

It is very simple. You believe in the young poem and the young poet.
Bullets and roses into your eyes. Poems. Inevitable poems. Inevitable poets.

Power To The Poets   Peace On Us All   Arnold Adoff
1971

i should have caught my unicorn when i was
sixteen
because to catch a unicorn you have to
trust
and believe
and love
all with an astonishing measure of innocence.
they're crafty beasts, unicorns,
with thin legs and thick manes
and some people say
their horns are gold.
i've lost my chance to catch my unicorn
now
I'm too old
and too
caught
myself.

barren
sterile
dying inside like dead already
and time it was it rained
and i cried but i'm tired now
like dead already.
time it was the snow fell deep
                          and sweet
                          and cool
and it was soft against my collar
but i'm tired now
like dead
already.
i lost another friend last month
but whocares anyway not i
it was me because i turned away
and cried again because it wasn't enough
nothing's ever enough anymore—
i remember a doorway openempty
with a cobweb full of dead flies and a

fat black spider
but the spider was dying too
because all the flies had gone away
i keep a dried white daisy in my deskdrawer
because i remember too much
but i'm tired
now
like dead
already.
time it was sand on a sterile salt beach
and the sounds were soundless
and naked in the wind i ran
but i'm tired now
like
dead
already.

in pain fear sorrow tears sadness and hotcold empty nights,
can you see me through the soundless night?
i am was will be can you see me
inside me outside
(naked whisperless night)
i am was will be can you see
inside you outside
will i see you through the soundless night?
can you see me will you see me
i am was will be
in laughter smiles near and warmcool nights
remember   (can you see
remember   can you see me
remember   can you see me through the

                         soundless

                                    night?)

          remember me.

```
    1
   +5
    6
```

```
      6
    +18
     24
```

```
      24
    +601
     625
```

```
    625
   +381
   1006
```

```
    1006
    +318
    1324
```

```
    1324
   -1324
       0
```

I feel so muggy

so slow

and

calm,

full of love and

understanding,

peace,

and just so damn free.

I want you   to read / Elaine Schwager

I want you	**to read**
the poems	**I write**
see the movies	**I make**
hear the music	**I listen**
to eat	**the food**
I cook	**take**
the walks	**I've taken**
touch	**the thoughts**
I think	**join**
the life	**I am**
living	**here**

the poet believes whoever he watches.

"an almost mystical self-transcendence
in sun"

the clear shape of black and gray
learning paths and stones
a dirt road that cuts its way
spending time in sun

the dark woods begin to see
sharpen and clear
the fine light in grass   the dim time in shadow
what dawn is this that captures shade?
what lawn is this whose summer is brown?
what noises are these that capture vision?

what black and white is this dream?

ask these questions very large
demand that music equal light

. . . so look for mist to cover sky
search cold air to recognize the turned pebbles,
dirt and leaves which cover being here.

All in air is touch   soft breeze
and sky
soft breeze   and light
soft breeze
and the silhouettes we make from sky.

like tiny rain drops
sweet in order
one by one
falling from someones
tin tan roof
the days of
my life fall and
splash in the past
like a puddle of
gutter rain
each crystal cannonball
alone and my own
and special
each one diluted
by death

1-A

**click clack
tile floors
smack polished
lips
the gravity
trips my shoes
a locked door
used to be news
the whole floor
is confined
we are all pigeons
waiting to fly free
as white dress
black miss
flashes
brassgold key
I'm learning
my soul
how to control
beauty**

1-B

I can believe
that I'm under a
grapevine
plucking berries
or in sunshine
along wind that
carries
me away
all by the ocean
in land and out
of water
I dreamed I dried
my hair on a
clothesline along
with moonshine
from the night before
when the moon dived
into the sea
and wet her hair
to dry with me

1-C

eye lined pools of sea grey glisten
gay and sorrow
and shaded feather forests hiding them
from other eye lakes looking
shy glance or fire glare
splashing back the sea side
stare
of those on shore
ones who hid their eyes before
and now with view and vision
fair
they're searching for the sight
of you
mary
and all your salt pool looks and
tears aren't rare
to ones who one time shared your
view

i boiled a green marble and when it cooled it reflected a distorted
                    kitchen
and shapes which were beautiful because they were untouched
the marble was god then.
in november i long to kneel in fields of other stallions
                    and worship the sun
(cry, then, amber girl, for twisted akhenaten who prayed to the
                    perfect sun)
in the full night when, reaching out, i touch the cheek of sleep and
                    cry to it
the night, because it holds endless possibilities
is god
much of the time an idea that god must be love hovers around my eyes
which turn grey then
i cling to all which i may not touch for fear of knowing
and if i find i cannot believe i will squeeze all these things through the
cracks of my soul
and sing them.

bitchice / Ellen Jenkins

an icicle of me
frozen in myself
stiff jointed
hack kneed
in a lousy attitude
    for comfort.

frustrated beyond
tears sobs anger sniffles
    into vinegar ice
acid snowflakes.
    beyond screaming, o hell
with it.

damn! / Ellen Jenkins

damn!
damndamndamndamndamn damn!
damn ignorance
damn fool
damn slums
damn nigger
damn you
damn god
damn

    me.

i had not begun to know:
   i saw my father across the street
   (red light: don't walk)
and i followed a pair of legs
on the side-   walk
          (green light)
These Are Light Years, Father
follow   the explosions
         of fire
from across the universe
in infinite, but interrupted,
blackness

Man across this river of steel,
I AM
             (glaring
from window displays
         screaming
from torn advertisements—
shadows of fantasy envelop me)
I left my father's fire,
searching for a pair of legs
(green light)
across the street desire
glowed from a stoplight within
i had not known to begin

1 + 1 = 2 / Bob Frisell

To Family

1

Morning came (with you) morning comes
it did and the ardent air

the dawn breaks
t-h-r-o-u-g-h

for all
and your
pain is pain

and soothe is
you

profound womb

2

match comes
comes the season for
becoming one
he bounces through
and you go away
together
bouncing

his mixture
of one in
known numbers
your mixture
too

time for creating
two creating
two

3

falling farther
you meet
    and the intrinsic hand shoves
    you to the corner
    and crushes
    and you are played backward
    and you are like a spring

        here you are

        and pain is pain
        opening opening

        sees out
            morning's there

4

the question remaining
    of prodigious questioning

    the mixture
    and two of "right"
    makes

    and /we/ go on
    bouncing with the original

5

the faces look up at him
    and his doing they say
    does
            (but)
    four creepers
        no top
        bouncing creepers
        through

        and questioning remains

it is singing into your eyes / anthology of new young poets

Fire air
Number talk
    the climb
    the climb to
       being
    10-foot midgets
Climbing talk
Nothing language
Fire air

       Tucked in the corner
         The core
         coming to the surface like
         a released cork

stopping
no longer
understanding
the game,

no longer able to explain reality's
tilted words; actions
like dead pinballs
    no score
    no flashing lights
    no bells ringing
    no

splitting the silence
the roaring grinding
machine of oil and gas
sputtering under you
now tamed smooth
you hard on its back
taking off
piercing the air and rain
goading on
the shining gleaming mass
feeding it
willing it as you decide
it is alive and terrible
and shrieks under such insistence
you ride hard
a passion ride
against time
will against will
you always winning
demanding it to yield
demanding more and more
pressing on ahead
ride
ride
on and on

**American flags
and dreams
in a velvet crowd
a crowd so safe
I lay back
and caressed
a field of flowers
you took my hand**

dawn / Norman Kaplan

dropped awake
like an ancient
into a shadow
no longer
than shame,
& no sooner
than joy
did i drop
warfare & money
to climb
into the daylight
of your name.

rusty come home damn you
your mommy misses you and so do i
and don't worry
i don't care
how long your hair is
what you've done
where you are or any of that other rot,
just come home.
i don't understand
where or when or why you're going
and anyway i miss you rusty
please
come home
damn you.

i wish i could stay with you awhile
but the sunshine's coming near
    (a prophet told me once
    that i could hear
    your heart by mine
    or hold the oceans in my hand)
understand me when i say
now i must go
you know
i never planned it this way
but a prophet told me once
i must go on
to the edges of the sun.

They tell you
Shadows are the place
To hide,
But listen:
No one
Looks into the sun.

after any sunset
there is a glint
a certain afterglow
a rainbow show
of starflake snow
some dim glimmer
of sweet evening
shimmer
after any sunset
the end of day
the end of love
the end of living
a soft celebration
of once holding
now that is passed

born of leaf and branch
  in the pale orange
  sunset
natural sheet of light
     the sky
is gray and blue
with cloud
     trees
with arms bent toward the sun
and the sun answers with leaving
     green to black and
sounds no longer exist
dark-blue swallows pale orange
     for in darkness must be
the thought of day
in the mandrake
madonna's womb

gone my mission

sun in heaven

alone,

a

phantom of

gone lights and

wrong missions,

I

hear the echoes of

the acheron passengers

dreaming

nothing

cadences

II.

**won't you/won't you
make it
last
the day
is like
honey
with tincture
of emerald
jewels
sparkling
like torn mirrors
from yr
clay-still
face . . .**

the time
is just
lit up
with whispered
echoes
of eastern
words
seeping
through the
worn-out cracks
of a western
dream,
amphetamine conversation
into the eternity
of forgotten faces
& floating moments
of a season
just now
gone
but not quite
over,
the sun still
breathing
into the
fire-coated
sky . . .

I feel the sun
I feel the air

the red grass buzzes and the flowers begin

TO BLOOM: finally, next to the rocks
next to the stones
next to the bottlecaps
next to the gold
next to the yellowyellow grass
next to the goldgold sun

finally, it's summer in a field,
next to the hot heavy sweet blue
of the air
think about some dusty earth
think about some dusty earth

think about lying on melting stone
when you feel the red heat
on your back
when you feel the red heat on your legs

when you feel the red heat
on your breasts

oh summer
　　　the heavy heavy mist
　　　　　the melting air

　　　　　　　　Oh
　　　　　warm salty sweat
　　　dust earth and stones
　　　　　　flowers
　gold
　　　Oh golden warm
　　　　　　rocks　　gold
　　oh hot heavy　misting air
　　　　　　　　　feeling
　　　thank god for the summer
　　　　　the sweet hot air.

it is the poem into your eyes / anthology of new young poets

bone sweet
tangled lines of hair as true
as the form of moon
and fire
lashes blown wild to touch
weaver's hands to seek
a loom
ocean eyed
waiting for each
one of us
to confess
through sad rushes
and frightened poems
waiting for the fine
filigree
of prayer.
In anger
and in pain
(still bone sweet)
drinking wine and milk
burning
soundlessly
crushed on the crest
of bitterest anger—
an anger also sweet
to recall my purpose
(was it to name you soulless
and a thief?)
i watch you
remembering slowly
your face.

When   gathering   up   on   the   wet   mountain   morning
        flowers purple   as   a   boy,   green   dew
the   one   day   gentle   breeze   looked   up   upon   the   morning
        green   and   purple
whose   buds   left   his   head   in   clouds
Stilted   as   uplifted   branches   his   fingers   grasp   to   gather
        green   and   purple
mind   twirling   as   he   runs   down   the   mountain

I gave / Mary Celinia Bruce

I gave
in springtime
steam wave
love to
love
in garden green
the sun glow
grassy sheen
of love
of
love
to one in
night time
place
the beauty
in his
moonlit face
I made
love
love
in spring fresh
air
the sly sweet
dare
of love
of
love

and star lace
played upon
his hair
and washed
the sails
of love
downstream
and cradled
far
my springtime
dream

vel
dwell in
the
dark
vet
set a star
to
spark
night is
a sail
a trail
a trip
upon a
day gone
ship
to dawn
tar from
star
and to
the lawn
black up
and back
Night is
a coal
a hole in
the bright
a wink
between the
blink of
light

Dream-song / Pam Murtha

woke up
a land of munchkins
carbon smile
on my eyelid
sun has in sanded shadow
etched tinder of your sound
in crevices of my hand
in yellow sand
remembering grass roots smell—
my nostril
—and your lips against my neck
woke up
and felt for your see
swung loose from the shore
think so loudly
"you be who—who are you?"

big ben recalled the evening
coded to my backbone
"he be judy garland's lover"

but i see
that you are
munchkin.

Nana pregnant
   Nana's pregnant
sing a song high up on a mountain
Nana baby gonna be smooth black tar
CLAP / CLAP
SIN / SAN / OOH / OOH / AH
baby of Nana have big full
lips of wisdom
                    oh   yeah
look at Nana   look   look
dancin so funny   look   look
with a baby in her belly
clap   Nana   stomp
clap   cause   Nana   havin   a   baby
                        oh   yeah

Sing yes, yes, yes,
To that first cooing night
Which spawns the greater self.
To that once hard brumal
Turned nascent
Night of lymph-like
Symposium, sing.
But then pray to no diety
Of this place and be
Without the cut of hope
Which is resignation.
The cicada's woo
Is no rasp
Is no blind curse
To my glad ears.

I am beautiful enough
And that sustains me.
There is a rough

Perfection in my colors—
My hair, so black; my faceskin, silver
Like a shivering

Moon. I twine willow
Branches through my hair,
I twist their lengths and sew

Them to my chest.
I reach pale edges,
Slipping over the crest

Of dark, shining stiff and dry,
Like a wafer nipple
In the beaded breast of night.

Brown and rust, I am the mother.
Ivory, I am the sister;
I can have no color as a lover.

I want no man to near me.
I want no man to break me;
Only my brother, white

And gold, to greet me at the dusk.

I have wound you an image
and laid it on waxy leaves.
I offer this gift, as it coils
on the green: a scalloped
milky serpent, slender and cool
with blue and silver seaming.
Press the narrow circlet
to your blind black hair.

I am white, I am white,
and my hair is static and cloudy.
I have no lucid colors;
only the faintly scrawled
signature of veins.
The jewelled tissue veils—
they are webs on me:
spun threads sealed to stiff limbs.

A cestus rings my waist;
it is strapped with ivory lacings
and traced with paling pearls.
It is meant to fade and fade.
You go to your swollen ladies
and in the dark you do not hear me come:
the dew of my blood
will lace the legs of men.

tumultuous diamond, with a spray
    of prism; you have left me. and
    the shattering rainbow
  gives off and away the new colors
we'd shared, red having
so many meanings.

said don't leave me here, in a sky / Jeff Heglin

said don't leave me here, in a sky
    gone lilac and smelling of a new
    spring and time when the shoots
    are white,
said don't bring me here, if a day
    goes yellow i will hate them all,
    and falling from the sky i will
    lose the garden,
    falling
(said i know, and i can't
        i can't. . .).

Today
I looked through a seagull's tail
to the sky
(to the sea)
Flying seagulls
fly
for me
to the clouds and
take a message
of love
   Love for flying things
     Love for lives of flying
       (not so high to lose the world
         but high enough to see it)
I have longed to be a seagull
Now I long to be the sky.

Watching the sky fall
rain
shaking bird
soon to be flown
away
If you could heartell
or see death's reversal
mirrored in tears
kissed now
blown and
it's an unusual Sunday
bathed in a sorrowful smile
soon to be dead.

Devil buried under
Sky blue
under
Brown lake
Childhood love
Once
Over blue
Sky
Black
Red moon

Dew drops.
.Flowers
Soon leafy trees!
Lovely poem always lifting, ,
Heaven sent this God forsaken planet is.

int. y●ur

the sun   hot
      and

  life
     in all smells
          and
     all sounds
          and
     all I see

black birds
    against a
       glaring sky
     and
    bugs crawling over me
      and

cows
   chewing
 we are   what   is
      and
all that is
   is us

Butterflies
    among clover
        as grasshoppers
           hop
        green frogs
        green pond water
        green reflections
           of

        gold sunshine
           early saturday sunshine
           early summer sun

The day we went out
to catch yellow butterflies
in mayonnaise jars and jar caps
and; to notice funny colored,
    funny shaped natures;
it rained cadillacs
all minutes;
and they were too heavy
for the trees,
so we all died.

we all joined a circle
to listen to the fire's old men chanting
to watch the wind's youth blow through the sparks

the aching crackles showing work
the wind howling to rebel
loosing direction and faith
and finally needing something to live

the circle grew too large
and all the ones whose turn next
       to the fire
       had come,

  began to burn.

now / Arthur Toegemann

now
when our last martyr died
it was sort of a disappointment
we couldn't find a cross
his size
and the one we finally got him
was much too large.

Graduation / John Heinegg

When the row in front of us sits
    We stand up
And wind single file for our diplomas.
    And when my name was read
And mispronounced
    I recalled my years of high school;
How my thoughts were carefully laundered
    And neatly pressed
And how nice it felt
    For my mind to slip smoothly between them
And fall asleep.

Circus / John Heinegg

The bus turned,
    Slithered down a side street
And was gone
      But I caught a glimpse of an advertisement
Pasted on its side
     Advertising
The Ringling Bros.
  steam shooting calliope three ring
 spotlighted M.C. with tuxedo leaping from trapeze
to trapeze among the tangled girders of the roof while trying
to look three ways at once as a string of elephants Barnum and
a tiny penlight on a keychain to play with in the stands and
break before the circus is over, cotton candy tigers are leaping,
stuck on your fingers and glueing your lips together
from stand to stand while bored lions look on and the canvas battleship
  with feet protruding beneath the hull, filing out
     and buying turtles or lizards in cardboard boxes
       which run away after a week or so Bailey
          and circus.

I.

Leaves, compress heat.
yes, the wind blew.
We came to *such* **buildings of brick**
passed
into and through.
the stairs.
brick.
bidden.
relieve me.
sharpness in the smell of cheese.

II.

cool water.
shoes in feet.
going down/stairs.
an unlocked door
enters a hall.
each image is slow horror

a lover of dull noise.

you thought the bed would be
w h i t e.
thought the *air* clear.
"found the fog,   grey."
mention:
slow
m o v e m e n t
stretch
travel slowly
speak definitions
be all pale
unravel silk
NOTICE THE SLANT OF LIGHT.
see my gaze
see my gaze

gaze.

everything I have learned.
the moon.
white icing bands his house.
out of the upper windows
and into the light is thrown not
a bird but a doll.
bless me says the child in the air
to snow melting now.
Thrown into the air
her cinders are falling down.
could we ask when she will hit the ground
or when does the air cease?
each answer is no.
the circle of rotations is the lady being
thrown and falling, always, into the air.
this air, being thrown and falling, like
skin breaking in warmth.
nothing can be stretched too far.
his movements are the sudden ones
climbing the side of the house.
can you say he wants to come in?
not yet.

they placed the blame on the doors and locks
but the fault in the house was why he left.
behind the panels promised as walls
the stairs in his dreams
say what I mean is not the child
falling out and down
not the flaws of the face in the light,
scaling and clawing the side of the house,
but the dizzy ooze and crush of snow,
the rotten water running from the pressure of the air.
damp has been put out of the walls.
the stone pores promise the dust of a sponge,
the only rain that will fall.
these are the walls he is climbing.
What he wants to do is climb to the window,
crawl inside,
and let the dust throw him
like a silver arc,
down and down into the sun.

**What are you doing
in the chimney
with your hat on
watching night
slay the dragon**

Tangling words
in music
> **patterns**
> **afraid of being**
perfect give up
enough to ask for
> **but not asking**
> **to deserve**
to need. This matter
a mouth speaks to
> **itself opening**
> **what it wants**
you to know
breaks
> **a sky, white**
> **and solid**
with a landscape
of words
> **singing**
> **betraying me**

with praise
you made
> **to make me**
> **love the sun**
for standing
behind
> **turning around**
> **I want**
to run
knowing
> **you are there**
> **toward it**
earning
love

n. (self-portrait)

waiting by the
          window

she
         waiting
by the window

she waits for the people
       the quivering blurred rainbows

to harden: iceglassarcs
       they cut her eyes and she turns.

                bleeding eyes.

o.

There   he
stretched brilliant
(like a slender stem)
in the simple grass,
sharp eye lines and mouth lines pressed into shining squints
of smiles,
touching me with the gold-and-ice breath of his skin

grass in his blueblack hair

p. (double image)

Two fragile ribbons—
plumsatin

          and velvet persimmon—
weave sun-dappled curves through the
  billowing   wide skirts of green:
His ivory-gray skin
    milk-streaked black eyes
you, soft sparks of beige
    around his face.

q.

waterribbon rainbows—
        his voice—
fall into the soft silver lake of my face,
colors twisting on clear splashes,
low tones—the sharp ridges in his
ebony hair,
shattering dew and tears on
my cheek.

r. (to notice a distance)

out and stunned
by honeysuckle breath
we
stretch on yellow-tipped green:
  two milky petals clasped still
            to a stem—

so long since our
edges   have touched.

The house, annoyed,
spits me out.
She says that I make her sides ache,
that I bother her with my noise
like a fly hurling against a window,
groping in funny dances
for an opening.
I will stay in the shade
because the colors are calmer there,
the trees wear little russet sleeves
spangled in chips of amethyst.
And the green washes everywhere,
liquid, loud,
so perfect it could be black.
In the land around the shadows,
sunlight dies in an open field.
There are only a few trees
and they are bone-slender,
as cracked and white
as the skin on my arm.

My hair is heavy and cool around me,
      like a tired silent stream
      folding over a barren mosaic of broken life.
My face lies at the bottom,
      scattered on a bank of yellow clay,
      its rocky lines distorted by the perfect water.
My face is stripped and clean,
      so ugly and sharp in its absolute and sole dimension,
      the different parts singing in one dull and toneless voice,
      broken only once by soft, muffled, sliding notes of
the pearls which tremble in the naked sockets of my eyes.
(I am drowned
      and my bones have drifted through the thick sea air
      and broken to ashen rock, they have been worn by the fish
      with their swollen bellies; speckled, fat as pears)

The boundary wriggles away
and pushes me into the
oatmeal brightness:
hard
yellow
yellow

      and only the dog watches, from a window.

it is the poem singing into your eyes / of new young poets

The man who

came

in

said the world could be

all right

and showed me a picture

of a

girl and

boy kneeling with some

pigs

and

chickens

near a new red barn (in an all right world).

the children   they move   stand
   about   roam freely
    come rushing,
       their innocence
   solemn
      their grace

have you seen them have you
   seen them
can you feel   the Revolution
Clear   as the sun   that makes
     the morning   blossom
Flowing and Brilliant
      through circles & meadows
     & on into
      Streets . . .

it does, it does, i have seen it
bleeding, brothers & sisters, i
have seen it, i have seen it,
come rushing, walk crippled,
fall flatly on tears of sad streets
where creatures fall onward with
cold eyes over them, armies on
streets over them, police on
pavements over them, tear gas
in faces over them, fires &
minds, living dreams living,
all of them innocents, yes,
yes, i have seen it, it bleeds,
it bleeds, have seen it bleed,
spill blood at my brothers,
cough no at our dignity,
i tell you, i tell you, we must,
kick on this monster, till it
dies, till it dies, dies, dies,
dies, dies, lies in the dirt
with its blood & its sickness,
head fall rolling in gutter,
red, white, & blue, flow freely,
flow freely, move over, fall down,
down, down, be finished at
last.

AMERICA THE BEAUTIFUL / Jean Streich

```
  IO   POLLUTION POLLUTION POLLUTION POLLUTION POLLUT
 TIO   POLLUTION POLLUTION POLLUTION POLLUTION POLLUTIO
UTIO   POLLUTION POLLUTION POLLUTION POLLUTION POLLUTIO
UTION  POLLUTION POLLUTION POLLUTION POLLUTION POLLUTIO
UTION  POLLUTION POLLUTION POLLUTION POLLUTION POLLUTIO
UTION  POLLUTION POLLUTION POLLUTION POLLUTION POLLUTIO
UTION  POLLUTION POLLUTION POLLUTION POLLUTION POLLUTIO
UTION  POLLUTION POLLUTION POLLUTION POLLUTION POLLUTIO
UTION  POLLUTION POLLUTION POLLUTION POLLUTION POLLUTIO
LUTION POLLUTION POLLUTION POLLUTION POLLUTION POLLUTIO
LUTION POLLUTION POLLUTION POLLUTION POLLUTION POLLUTIO
LUTION POLLUTION POLLUTION POLLUTION POLLUTION POLLUTIO
LUTION POLLUTION POLLUTION POLLUTION POLLUTION POLLUTIO
LUTION POLLUTION POLLUTION POLLUTION POLLUTION POLLUTIO
LUTION POLLUTION POLLUTION POLLUTION POLLUTION POLLUTIO
LUTION POLLUTION POLLUTION POLLUTION POLLUTION POLLUTIO
LUTION POLLUTION POLLUTION POLLUTION POLLUTION POLLUTIO
LUTION POLLUTION POLLUTION POLLUTION POLLUTION POLLUTIO
LUTION POLLUTION POLLUTION POLLUTION POLLUTION POLLUTIO
 UTION POLLUTION POLLUTION POLLUTION POLLUTION POLLUTIO
 UTION POLLUTION POLLUTION POLLUTION POLLUTION POLLUTIO
 UTION POLLUTION POLLUTION POLLUTION POLLUTION POLLUTIO
 UTION POLLUTION POLLUTION POLLUTION POLLUTION POLLUTIO
  TION POLLUTION POLLUTION POLLUTION POLLUTION POLLUTIO
   ION POLLUTION POLLUTION POLLUTION POLLUTION POLLUTIO
    ON POLLUTION POLLUTION POLLUTION POLLUTION POLLUTIO
                              ION PO    TION POLLUTIO
                               ON P       ON POLLUTIO
                                           N POLLUTIO
                                             POLLUTIO
                                             OLLUTIO
                                             LLUTIO
                                              UTIO
```

```
OLL                                                          TION
OLLU                                                        UTION
OLLUTION POLLUT                                           LLUTION
OLLUTION POLLUT                                       N POLLUTIO
OLLUTION POLLUT                                   UTION POLLUTI
OLLUTION POLLUT                        ION POLLUTION POLLUT
OLLUTION POLLUT                      TION POLLUTION POLLU
OLLUTION POLLUTION POLLUTION POLLUTION POLLU
OLLUTION POLLUTION POLLUTION POLLUTION POLLU
OLLUTION POLLUTION POLLUTION POLLUTION POLLUTI
OLLUTION POLLUTION POLLUTION POLLUTION POL
OLLUTION POLLUTION POLLUTION POLLUTION PO
OLLUTION POLLUTION POLLUTION POLLUTION P
OLLUTION POLLUTION POLLUTION POLLUTION
OLLUTION POLLUTION POLLUTION POLLUTION
OLLUTION POLLUTION POLLUTION POLLUTION
OLLUTION POLLUTION POLLUTION POLLUTION
OLLUTION POLLUTION POLLUTION POLLUTION POLL
OLLUTION POLLUTION POLLUTION POLLUTION POLL
OLLUTION POLLUTION POLLUTION POLLUTION P
OLLUTION POLLUTION POLLUTION POLLUTION
OLLUTION POLLUTION POLLUTION POLLUTI
OLLUTION POLLUTION POLLUTION POLLUT
OLLUTION POLLUTION POLLUTION POLLUT
OLLUTION POLLUTION POLLUTION POLLUT
OLLUTION POLLUTION POLLUTION POLLUT
OLLUTION PO              LUTION POLLUT
O          PO              N POLLUTI
           POLL              POLLUTIO
                            POLLUTIO
                           OLLUTION
                          LLUTION  P
                         LUTION  PO
                          TION  PO
                           ION  P
```

it occurred to me that we were driving
along the red and white stripes of the
flag, moving slowly through America.
Somewhere into blue-starred Baltimore
nites, about to meet the heart and soul
of the country, we were laid upon the
land in cloth-like consistency, a
little frayed at the edges but waving
as much as ever.

They run up and down the corridors
        looking through the windows
        knocking at the doors
        waiting for the people
The people hear
but do not come
        no one
        ever
        comes
Why is there no black in the red, white, and blue?

THE POO-LICE / Nelson Brown (Ameer)

WE SAVE
WE PROTECT
EVERYBODY . . . . . . WITH THE MAN
ANYBODY . . . . WITH THE MAN
AND MONEY
$$$$$$$
$$$$$$$
$$$$$$
$$$$$
$$$$
$$$
$$
$
NO MONEY (no sale)
POOR PEOPLE "DON'T HOLLER POO-LICE"
BIG STICKS
TWO GUNS (.357 Magnums)
WE SERVE THE PEOPLE

ON A 7' by 3'
STEEL AND WOODEN SLAB
COUNTY MORGUE
8:00 DOA
SERVED
DIAL A PRAYER
PO 5-1313
SATAN'S BIG FISTED SLAVES
WILL BE THERE
TOO LATE
POO-LICE

MINDLESS, MACHINES
MENACING AND MASACARING
MURDERING AND MOLESTING
MEN / WOMEN / CHILDREN
SERVING AND PROTECTING

THE MAN

12:15 Ask not what your country

Remember: innocence and comfortable

indifference

melting into

12:26 thought, awareness

Remember: slogans and chants

protest

12:43 The night had blackened

camera lights flashed

on nightsticks

there was red . . .

experience.

Frank Sawyer
70
who has been in
prison
39 years
for a bank robbery
was granted a full
pardon
today
by Kansas
Gov. Docking, who said he
believed Sawyer
was telling
the truth.

Frank Sawyer
70

who has been in prison
39 years

was granted a full pardon
today

Frank Sawyer
who has been in prison
39 years

Frank Sawyer
70

was granted a full pardon
today.

O'Neil the undertaker drives the
mirror black limousine
one hand on the wheel
elbow out the window flicking ashes
from his half-burnt cigarette
O'Neil makes sure he seats the
whole family in the same mirror black
limousine, tries to isolate them
from the others
O'Neil has plush carpet steps
with secret lint in the corners
the most beautiful place
in town
the night before, O'Neil
polishes the deep oak casket
shines the six brass handles
O'Neil covers the body
with silk sheets
hides the face with a
silver mesh screen to distort
the plastic cheeks which he,
O'Neil himself, moulded
arranges the chairs in neat
rows of six
then opens the door
at 7:30 sharp

"keep to the right" O'Neil directs
tries to comfort his customers
by a hearty hand clasp
a smile and a pack of advertising matches
then hurries back to check the
supply of Maxwellhouse coffee
keeps on smiling

and on Sunday morning
O'Neil ushers at church
"keep to the right" he directs
and passes the collection basket
after church O'Neil greets
his customers with a
hearty hand clasp and a smile
and more advertising matches
then drives home in his
mirror black limousine
and on Sunday nights when
most families prepare for another
week
O'Neil stays home
and cries

Good clean whiteman's fun
    to scalp
America of its heathen,
We burn down the teepees
Smoke their peyote and wear the feathers,
We paint them white with war paint;
Good clean whiteman's fun
    to be saviors
to the heathen
We give them 40 luxury reservations
tax-free with starvation and disease,
the missionaries count their church alms.
We are destroying the cult;
Where is the Almighty Great Spirit?

opity the indian on
    seein but not
           them billowed sails
the threat lost to innocence
    the forest   to the ship

The place is here.
This is the place time has
long forgotten,
Deep in the woods, this lone-
deserted swamp land
Where men have lived and died.

No one knows our dream, our desire,
They don't know of our love or hate.
No, they don't know.
No one knows.
To them we are washed away
with the floods.
But our life is here
Lost or won.

Ah democracy.
Freedom and justice for all.
A government that is run
by the people. It's
such a lavish dream.

1776–1970 / John Zeier

We, the people of the United States,
in order to form a more perfect Union,
establish justice, insure domestic trauillty,
provide for the comma defencse,
pro mote the general welfar,
and secure th e belsiggings of libty,
toour sel ves and ou rpostenerty,
do or dai n and establishjm
thisn Con slip crit ion of th eU.Sa

Art le 1 A od , w9 : 27$Klng) 7$ 1djiW
/a

of e

If you jam an atom bomb
Up your nose,
S l i c e   open
your
      stomach,

      plunge   a fire hose
into your mouth,
Squirt nitro-glycerin
                        down

      your
left   ear,
Stick dynamite
                  between   your   toes,
Flame fire
Through your eyes, and everything
either burns, infects or explodes;

Do you know what happens?

Your head
Burns red
and your brains
squirt out.

let us make war
   with our mouths
   and tongues instead of guns
     and bullets.
hands were made to
   hold different barrels
and stocks than those
   of a rifle.
let us fight to the
   death of our desires.

I reach;
> can't touch.

You aren't there.   I had a dream.
You reached too
but you were nothing but a hand.
What is a hand?
It was made to pluck flowers for my hair,
hold my face,
caress my lips,
to be soft and loving,
to write sonnets in honor of our love,
to embrace me when I'm depressed.
It was a nightmare.
I could touch but wouldn't.
Your hand was dirty,   calloused,   and lying in a pool of blood,
with a rifle for a body.

I know you wanted
my mornings,
but there was a war.
I was
    part of the bullets
    with the sound
    of shells
    that went into
    your body.

I tasted the grass
on the front lines
and the blood.
I felt you wanting
    the knees
    that were in
    the mud
    and the eyes
    in the killings
being parted
like the blades
into the violence
that they gave us.

I was
with the torments
of reacting earths
in the dusks
where the noises
lessened to the stars
and the dead
corpsed the weeds
into sudden nights.

taps
I pull up my blanket

around me

turn inside of me

alone
with my thoughts

we wander

The evening shadows, crisp and clandestine,
Fall across the haggard mortar lines.
The rattling sun, half-fallen and bloodshot,
Casts itself on rifle butts.
Wretched profiles spread against the marigold.
A shell rises and splinters
Over the folds of hills and over the apple orchards
Rotting in a black wind.

**The Defense Dept.
has announced the names of
18
U.S. servicemen killed in action
in Vietnam
in its latest list:
They included
Army 2nd Lt. William M. Lyons
killed
Marine Pfc. Jerry Sylvia
killed
William
killed
Jerry
killed
18
killed**

Ugly Day / Martin Levine

Don't make me go. I never said I wanted walking in that harsh gray cloud of file,
that zapping, stinging stuff injecting sparks
of pain. I clutch my wrapping, tinsel ar-
mor, but the spiky world still grates me like
a carrot (lord, the world is falling in,
the sky is falling in). The ugly (marks-
man) day rips trembling leaves, zips them like bullets, splats them like clay pigeons. Let me in.
(Good God, I hope some spartan doesn't say,
"Open the window; let some fresh file in.")
But close in, cosy in our warm. Close out
the ugly day. Close in the clean white walls
and comfy in your armchairs, you curl smoke
and talk The War out. (silent plea: Don't make
me face the ugly day alone, the ug-
ly world alone. Don't War—Together face
our common enemy.)

Clear Today,
younger,
invisible,
many places
& gone.

Everybody's winter
& left by violence . . .
at night huddle
& in day
light.

People singing
eyes.

Making peace
& the imaginary beings
of desires.

Trumpets circling
breathless, senseless
vagrant streets & mountains
of cries.

No one coming home.

Soft skin
children.

(Ghosts of faces
jagged, unsteady,
float in;
remaining,
the starved.)

See the accident!

Bellies full of hun-
ger.

The mirror of tears
smashed
to jagged,
unsteady
pieces
on the floor of your face.

**The child ate worms
A jealous bird drank warm milk;
change can be balanced.**

Breaking open buds / Kate Ballen

**Breaking open buds
Thorns prick my slipping fingers;
flowers drink the blood.**

it is the poem singing into your eyes / anthology of new young

today
today
it
it finally happened
they
they found
they got
the one
who
took my black
sister's
life away from
her
as
if it was
nothing more than
a
piece of
paper
flying in the
wind

i
i black power
saluted
him
him
my soul brother
i
stepped
out around
the corner after
dark
him knocked
me in
the head
&
robbed me
him still my brother

blackman
he's
superman
he
black
he
don't
ever get tired
him
a
machine
wind
him up
&
watch him perform
for you unreal people
see how he
can run/jump
he's
been doing it for four hundred
      years
him still
ain't tired
but
if
i
were you unreals
i wouldn't
keep on winding
him up
him might come
            alive

Little bird   got a name
You call it sparrow
Drop of water got a name
You call it rain
She is a woman
But it's slave you call her
You've seen her face
Don't you know her name?

i'm tired
of the man and his system
i realize it's late
but not too late
to take back
what is rightfully mine
you see
i am a Black Woman
and i love a Black Man
that is why i will
blow
(without regards for her long blond hair)
the brains out
of any young/white/liberal-minded girl
who tries to take his hand
and find

the Black Experience

all of a part of the people
experiencing the same hurt
that day we were told about
world hunger.
six hundred thirty-five dead every hour.
this is to you
the girl with the kind work boots.
turning to listen closer into the words
we accidentally touched
(your feet and my back)
i remember you speaking in soft tones in back of me,
to a friend beside you—
interrupting only to say
i'm sorry.
actually, i think it was my fault
if it was, i'm glad
had i not touched you
we would never have shared a smile.

**we breathed each other in
(to protect)
and let each other out
(to discover his own kind of freedom).**

Love is a cushion against the street
and the street world,
and the big heat
that pounces like the striped jungle cat;
and the cold, the stalking cold
that creeps in slow and freezes first,
then kills.
Love is a yellow voice;
a hand hovering between the light and dark,
motionless in the gray world,
the limbo world of shadows,
of dream shapes and half realities.
Love is a buffer,
a backwash
where the sea comes trailing in like a bird
with copper on its wings.
Love is a jellied mouth,
and a downy head resting,
Love is a cushion.

Hit hard;
hit fast;
draw blood, lion, roar.
Fate's a whore.
Walk tough; walk proud.
Street face; talk loud.
Never stop . . .
cop all that your hands can cop,
but never stop.
Don't sigh; don't frown.
Never let them beat you down.

I Am Cool Brother Cool / William Alfred McLean, Jr.

I ain't scared
he think he the pro, honey
but when I had a fight with him
I made him cry, that's true.

When I'm cool, I think I'm bad.
I put on this funny look on my face
my eyeballs—my eye.

I tell a girl a cool rap.
I cool rapped her one day on the stairway.
I had on all black
I cut off the lights.

I diddily bop when I go,
when I see my girl
(I can't tell her name
I might get in trouble).

When I get money like five dollar
I take her to the movies
on Saturday sometimes.
I come in there
I have these pink pants on—
all pink.

I saw this dope addict
I was with my sister
sometimes we go to the store at night
I carry this iron pipe with me
sometimes people be hiding in dark alleys
in the school yard

I be snapping my finger.

Stickball
          Stickball
hit the ball
run the streets
hope no
Brand new Eldorado Cadillac
runs you over
          Stick ball
          Stick ball
          hit the ball and hope you
          play stick ball
another   night.

Their

lives

don't

touch

mine.

Going to his grave
Who cares
dreams would be heavy
if
you had an airtank on
your back

no. no.
job man.
black. no job man.
he. man sitting.
in a trash can alley.

no man.
he is not dead.
no man.
he is not dying.
he is lying there because he has
no where else to go.
it is Christmas time man.
and just to think that on this
day he has no where else to go.
man.
man,
man.
are you listening to me.
no. no. man. don't pick him up.
let him lay.
it is his Christmas.
let him have his corner.

Index to Authors

Figures in parentheses denote poet's age when poem was written.

123

Index to First Lines

Index to Titles